From Home to School 1

Stories and Activities for Parents

Workbook

D1484649

Ann Gianola

Instructor, San Diego Community College District
San Diego, California

New Readers Press

From Home to School Workbook Level 1
ISBN 1-56420-302-6
Copyright © 2003 New Readers Press
New Readers Press
Publishing Division of ProLiteracy Worldwide
1320 Jamesville Avenue, Syracuse, New York 13210

Printed in the United States of America
9 8 7 6 5 4 3

All proceeds from the sale of New Readers Press materials
support literacy programs in the United States and worldwide.

Acquisitions Editor: Paula Schlusberg
Series Editor: Terrie Lipke
Production Director: Heather Witt
Designer: Kimbrly Koennecke
Illustrations: Brian Wallace, James P. Wallace
Production Specialist: Alexander Jones
Cover Design: Shelagh Clancy

Contents

Underline the Correct Verb

1. I (<u>feel</u>/feels) tired this morning.

2. The children (don't/doesn't) want to get up.

3. Does the boy (want/wants) to sleep?

4. We (don't want/doesn't want) to miss the school bus.

5. Mother (look/looks) at the clock.

6. Jessica eats breakfast and (brush/brushes) her teeth.

7. They (run/runs) to the bus stop.

8. The girls (yell/yells), "Wait!"

9. The bus driver (stop/stops) and (open/opens) the door.

10. (Is/Are) you lucky today?

You Write the Question

1. <u>*Do you feel tired today?*</u>   Yes, I feel tired today.

2. _____   No, I don't want to get up.

3. _____   Yes, the bus comes at 7:15.

4. _____   No, the bus isn't leaving.

5. _____   Yes, I am lucky this time.

Match Words and Pictures

| get dressed | brush teeth | ✔ comb hair |

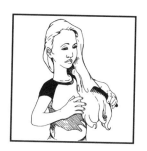

1. <u>comb hair</u>

2. _____

3. _____

Matching: Opposites

__f__ **1.** morning   **a.** open

____ **2.** dressed   **b.** early

____ **3.** lucky   **c.** slowly

____ **4.** quickly   **d.** put down

____ **5.** closed   **e.** stopped

____ **6.** coming   **f.** evening

____ **7.** pick up   **g.** undressed

____ **8.** late   **h.** going

____ **9.** asleep   **i.** unfortunate

____ **10.** started   **j.** awake

Check the Correct Picture

1.

a. _____ b. _✔_

3.

a. _____ b. _____

2.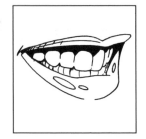

a. _____ b. _____

4.

a. _____ b. _____

Underline the Time You Hear

1. 7:15   7:50   **7.** 10:05   10:15

2. 2:30   3:20   **8.** 12:30   2:20

3. 9:40   9:14   **9.** 8:07   8:27

4. 1:10   1:30   **10.** 4:00   4:40

5. 3:31   3:41   **11.** 11:55   11:25

6. 6:40   6:45   **12.** 5:08   5:00

How Is the *e* Pronounced?

✔ be	breakfast	Emily	sees	yellow
bed	dressed	need	sleep	yells
begins	eats	opens	teeth	

feels

1. ___be___
2. _____
3. _____
4. _____
5. _____
6. _____
7. _____

get

1. _____
2. _____
3. _____
4. _____
5. _____
6. _____
7. _____

Matching: Times

____ **1.** 6:45

____ **2.** 10:15

____ **3.** 9:30

____ **4.** 12:00

____ **5.** 4:10

____ **6.** 8:50

a. nine thirty

b. twelve o'clock

c. eight fifty

d. six forty-five

e. four ten

f. ten fifteen

Write Short Answers

1. Is the nurse doing eye exams now?   Yes, <u> she is   </u>.

2. Is it my turn?   No, _____.

3. Are you covering your left eye?   Yes, _____.

4. Is the third line easy to read?   No, _____.

5. Are the letters too small?   Yes, _____.

6. Can you see the board?   No, _____.

7. Do you get headaches?   Yes, _____.

8. Do your eyes feel tired?   No, _____.

9. Is this letter from the nurse?   Yes, _____.

10. Does she need glasses?   No, _____.

Write the One-Word Comparative

1. The first line is (easy) <u> easier   </u> to read than the last.

2. Do the letters on the left look (big) _____ than the letters on the right?

3. The board looks (clear) _____ when I wear my glasses.

4. The words in the newspaper are (small) _____ than the words in this book.

Underline the Correct Word

1. It's time for your eye (exam/examine).

2. It is his (tired/turn) now.

3. Please cover your (write/right) eye.

4. Can you read the letters on the (second/sending) line?

5. The letters on the (chair/chart) are too small.

6. Can you see the (board/bored) in the classroom?

7. Does he copy things (wrong/wrote)?

8. Layla's eyes feel tired, and she gets a (headache/backache).

9. Layla gives the letter to her (patients/parents).

10. You need to visit the (yes/eye) doctor.

Matching: Meanings

_____ 1. exam   **a.** mother and father

_____ 2. difficult   **b.** test

_____ 3. small   **c.** pain in the head

_____ 4. below   **d.** hard

_____ 5. wrong   **e.** incorrect

_____ 6. headache   **f.** little

_____ 7. parents   **g.** under

Check the Correct Picture

1.

a. _____   b. _____

3.

a. _____   b. _____

2.

a. _____   b. _____

4.

a. _____   b. _____

Underline the Word You Hear

1. week   work

2. sitting   seating

3. left   leave

4. easy   each

5. small   smell

6. fourth   fifth

7. stop   step

8. see   sees

9. tire   tired

10. nurse   nervous

11. right   ride

12. eyes   ice

How Is the Final *s* Pronounced?

| ✔charts | exams | lines | reads | stops |
| covers | headaches | points | sometimes | weeks |

s

1. _charts_
2. _____
3. _____
4. _____
5. _____

z

1. _____
2. _____
3. _____
4. _____
5. _____

Write the Words

Ordinal numbers show the order of things. Write the words for the ordinal numbers from 1 through 10.

1. _first_
2. _____
3. _____
4. _____
5. _____

6. _____
7. _____
8. _____
9. _____
10. _____

Write the Correct Question Word

Who	Where	How

1. ___Where___ are they from? They are from Mexico.

2. _____ do you feel today? I feel fine today.

3. _____ does the boy feel? He feels shy.

4. _____ is your teacher? My teacher is Mrs. Shaw.

5. _____ do I sit? Sit at table three.

6. _____ can speak Spanish? Eva can speak Spanish.

Change *She* to *They*

1. She is 8 years old. ___They are 8 years old.___

2. She is from Russia. _____

3. She sees many children. _____

4. She feels shy. _____

5. She sits at table three. _____

6. She has a new friend. _____

Match Words and Pictures

enter class	sit down	point to chair

1. _____   2. _____   3. _____

Matching: Opposites

____ **1.** first   **a.** exits

____ **2.** new   **b.** nervous

____ **3.** enters   **c.** difficult

____ **4.** many   **d.** old

____ **5.** sits   **e.** stands

____ **6.** empty   **f.** frown

____ **7.** easy   **g.** do

____ **8.** smile   **h.** few

____ **9.** calm   **i.** last

____ **10.** don't   **j.** full

Check the Correct Picture

1.

    a. _____   b. _____

3.

    a. _____   b. _____

2.

    a. _____   b. _____

4.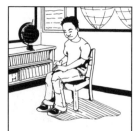

    a. _____   b. _____

Underline the Word You Hear

1. It is Juan's (first/fourth) day at school.

2. Is (he/she) from Mexico?

3. My daughter is only 11 (months/years) old.

4. (Everyone/No one) in the class speaks English.

5. We have a new (student/teacher).

6. Sit down at table number (two/three).

7. What does that word mean in (Spanish/English)?

How Is the *a* Pronounced?

came	day	name	table
can	have	Spanish	today
class	last	states	understand

late

1. _____
2. _____
3. _____
4. _____
5. _____
6. _____

at

1. _____
2. _____
3. _____
4. _____
5. _____
6. _____

Underline the Stressed Syllable

<u>Me</u>xico   begin   understand

Japan   Japanese   worry

everyone   language   speaking

teacher   across   united

empty   English   welcome

Write Tag Questions

1. You're getting ready for school, _aren't you_____ ?

2. We have time to eat, _____ ?

3. He likes cereal, _____ ?

4. I don't have time, _____ ?

5. Robert is going to eat at school, _____ ?

6. You ride the bus for 30 minutes, _____ ?

7. Catherine feels hungry, _____ ?

8. He isn't in the cafeteria, _____ ?

9. They serve lunch every day, _____ ?

Change *He* to *We*

1. He is getting ready now. _____

2. He needs to leave early. _____

3. He has no time to eat. _____

4. He is going to eat later. _____

5. He rides the school bus. _____

6. He is very hungry today. _____

Match Words and Pictures

catch the bus	leave the house	throw it away

1. _____   2. _____   3. _____

Matching: Meanings

____ **1.** pay attention to   **a.** place to get food

____ **2.** cereal   **b.** 12 months

____ **3.** son   **c.** travel on

____ **4.** understand   **d.** listen to

____ **5.** cafeteria   **e.** get the meaning of

____ **6.** speak   **f.** food or drink holder

____ **7.** container   **g.** male child

____ **8.** year   **h.** breakfast food

____ **9.** ride   **i.** with nothing in it

____ **10.** empty   **j.** talk

Check the Correct Picture

1.

　　a. _____　　　　b. _____

3.

　　a. _____　　　　b. _____

2.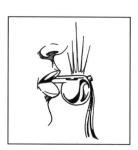

　　a. _____　　　　b. _____

4.

　　a. _____　　　　b. _____

Underline the Word You Hear

1. I catch the (train/bus) at 7:00.

2. Is your (father/mother) in the kitchen?

3. Do you have time for some (cereal/sausage)?

4. There is a breakfast (menu/program) at school.

5. He wants his (son/child) to stay healthy.

6. We (ride/arrive) at school at 7:25.

7. The (school/student) cafeteria is on the right.

Underline the Stressed Syllable

hungry	attention	today
breakfast	healthy	banana
office	begin	container
something	cereal	daughter
away	Tuesday	menu

Change the Singular to Plural

Check *s*, *z*, or *iz* to show the correct pronunciation of the final sound.

			s	z	iz
1. yellow house	_yellow houses_		___	___	✔
2. new school	_____		___	___	___
3. bus	_____		___	___	___
4. empty bowl	_____		___	___	___
5. heavy backpack	_____		___	___	___
6. program	_____		___	___	___
7. healthy son	_____		___	___	___
8. good student	_____		___	___	___
9. full glass	_____		___	___	___

Underline the Correct Verb

1. His mother (is/are) sitting in the classroom.

2. (Is/Are) they talking to the teacher?

3. Fernando (helps/help) Pedro with his homework.

4. I (am/are) happy that you are here today.

5. Mrs. Ramirez (feel/feels) proud of her son.

6. (Is/Are) reading and math difficult for him?

7. You (need/needs) to read more at home.

8. My children (don't/doesn't) watch a lot of TV.

9. We (is/are) worried about that too.

10. Pedro's father (take/takes) him to the library.

You Write the Question

1. _____? Yes, the conference is today.

2. _____? No, she isn't his teacher.

3. _____? Yes, I am proud of my child.

4. _____? No, he doesn't read at home.

5. _____? Yes, you can check out books.

Complete the Sentences

classroom	library	return
help	readers	✔ third

1. Our granddaughter is in the ___third___ grade.

2. Where is Miss Soto's _____ ?

3. She says that good students are also good _____ .

4. Find books about baseball in the public _____ .

5. You can _____ your daughters be good students.

6. Don't forget to _____ your books in two weeks.

Match Words and Pictures

Reading	Handwriting	Math

4+3=
6-2=
8+3=
10-7=

abcdef

1. _____   2. _____   3. _____

Underline the Day and Time You Hear

1. Monday at 1:30   Monday at 11:30   Sunday at 11:30

2. Thursday at 10:30   Tuesday at 10:30   Thursday at 3:10

3. Wednesday at 2:45   Wednesday at 12:45   Friday at 2:55

4. Saturday at 12:00   Saturday at 2:00   Sunday at 12:00

5. Friday at 4:00   Friday at 4:15   Friday at 4:45

6. Thursday at 6:00   Thursday at 7:00   Thursday at 5:00

7. Monday at 8:15   Monday at 8:45   Monday at 8:10

8. Tuesday at 3:30   Tuesday at 3:40   Tuesday at 3:50

Underline the Word You Hear

1. Is he in the (second/sixth) grade?

2. I need to talk to your (mother/brother).

3. The teacher is concerned about her (reading/writing).

4. He needs help with his (spelling/science).

5. Their daughter is (beside/behind) the other students.

6. She is (concerned/worried) about that too.

7. Reading is very (important/unimportant).

8. Look for a good book about (baseball/basketball).

Underline the Words

Underline the words that have the same vowel sound you hear in the word *it*.

<u>sitting</u>	nice	smile	little
difficult	important	library	behind
nine	principal	inches	triangle
mile	miss	interesting	right

Put these Authors' Names in Alphabetical Order

____ Donaldson	____ Pekras	____ Yang
____ Burich	____ Novak	____ Fujita
__1__ Aziz	____ Zimmerman	____ Davis
____ Mansour	____ Suero	____ King
____ Jimenez	____ Tran	____ Gallo
____ Walsh	____ Quimby	____ Bachman
____ Flynn	____ Ortega	____ Schmidt

Write Short Answers

1. Does Mrs. Yin volunteer in the class?   Yes, _____.

2. Is your son in the first grade?   No, _____.

3. Is she raising her hand?   No, _____.

4. Does Eve understand the problem?   Yes, _____.

5. Do you correct tests for the teacher?   No, _____.

6. Can you volunteer again tomorrow?   No, _____.

Write Each Sentence in the Negative

1. His daughter is in the fifth grade.

   His daughter isn't in the fifth grade. _____

2. She volunteers in her son's class.

   _____

3. He can come on Tuesday.

   _____

4. They understand the problem.

   _____

5. I can correct these papers.

   _____

Complete the Sentences

corrects	grade	proud	time
flashcard	groups	raise	volunteer

1. Please _____ your hand if you have a question.

2. I want to spend _____ in my son's classroom.

3. Is your child in the second _____ this year?

4. Ina feels _____ when her mother comes to school.

5. We need someone to _____ on Wednesday.

6. Hold up the _____ and ask, "What is 3 + 4?"

7. Mr. Lopez always _____ papers for the teacher.

8. Who will work with those _____ of children?

Matching: Days

____ **1.** Sunday   **a.** the day between Monday and Wednesday

____ **2.** Monday   **b.** three days after Monday

____ **3.** Tuesday   **c.** the day before Sunday

____ **4.** Wednesday   **d.** the day after Saturday

____ **5.** Thursday   **e.** two days before Sunday

____ **6.** Friday   **f.** the day between Tuesday and Thursday

____ **7.** Saturday   **g.** the day before Tuesday

Check the Correct Picture

1.

a. _____   b. _____

3.

a. _____   b. _____

2.

a. _____   b. _____

4.

a. _____   b. _____

Fill in the Addition Problems You Hear

1. 5 + _3_

2. ___ + 2

3. 8 + ___

4. ___ + 1

5. 3 + ___

6. ___ + 3

7. 1 + ___

8. ___ + 6

9. 7 + ___

10. ___ + 4

11. 0 + ___

12. ___ + 9

13. 5 + ___

14. ___ + 3

Underline the Words

Underline the words that have the same vowel sound
you hear in the word *grade*.

happy	raises	papers	small
addition	hand	aide	can
wake	asks	maybe	last
radio	phrase	that	explain

Change the Singular to Plural

Check *s* or *z* to show the correct pronunciation of
the final sound.

		s	z
1. small group	_____	___	___
2. classroom	_____	___	___
3. active volunteer	_____	___	___
4. difficult problem	_____	___	___
5. flashcard	_____	___	___
6. grade	_____	___	___
7. question	_____	___	___
8. addition fact	_____	___	___
9. proud parent	_____	___	___

Write the Correct Question Word(s)

Who	What	When	Where	How long

1. _____ does Juan open?   He opens his backpack.

2. _____ is the note from?   It is from Mr. Ryan.

3. _____ are the tests?   They are next week.

4. _____ kind of test is it?   It's a reading test.

5. _____ does the test take?   It takes two hours.

6. _____ do the children go?   They go to Room 6.

7. _____ is ready to begin?   Juan is ready to begin.

8. _____ is Juan's bedtime?   Juan's bedtime is 8:00.

Write the Two-Word Comparative

1. This exam is (difficult) _more difficult_____ than the practice test we took yesterday.

2. It is (important) _____ to listen than to talk.

3. This breakfast is (nutritious) _____ than the one we had yesterday.

4. Zack looks (tired) _____ than John right now.

Match Words and Pictures

backpack	breakfast	bedroom

1. _____ 2. _____ 3. _____

Matching: Meanings

____ **1.** grade

____ **2.** next

____ **3.** suggests

____ **4.** bed

____ **5.** tired

____ **6.** arrive

____ **7.** early

____ **8.** ready

____ **9.** test

____ **10.** every

a. proposes

b. class in school

c. weary

d. before the usual time

e. following at once

f. prepared

g. get to

h. place to sleep

i. each one

j. exam

Check the Correct Picture

1.

a. _____   b. _____

3.

a. _____   b. _____

2.

a. _____   b. _____

4.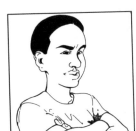

a. _____   b. _____

Write the Times You Hear

1. _____   8. _____

2. _____   9. _____

3. _____   10. _____

4. _____   11. _____

5. _____   12. _____

6. _____   13. _____

7. _____   14. _____

Underline the Words

Underline each word that has the same vowel sound you hear in the word *go*.

opens	who	low	road
phone	note	home	good
those	school	notebook	on
mother	from	forget	not
to	only	you	out
holiday	copy	month	long
Monday	also	other	got

Underline the Stressed Syllable

backpack	ready	language
activity	permission	arrive
material	announcement	important
principal	volunteer	result
information	student	understand
suggests	Friday	difficult

Write Tag Questions

1. Alfonso picks up Marla after school, _____?

2. Marla can sign up for soccer, _____?

3. The youth center is open, _____?

4. The children are playing soccer, _____?

5. She wants to play, _____?

6. The children wear uniforms, _____?

7. You don't play basketball, _____?

8. He doesn't know how much money it costs, _____?

9. He knows where the field is, _____?

10. You can call her parents, _____?

Change *He* to *I*

1. He picks up Marla. _____

2. He sees children playing. _____

3. He buys a soccer ball. _____

4. He doesn't know the cost. _____

5. He needs more information. _____

6. He can't say yes or no. _____

Complete the Sentences

cost	parents	play	time
field	pick up	soccer	uniform

1. How much does it _____ to play that sport?

2. Call her _____ if you have any questions.

3. He doesn't know the day and _____ of practice.

4. Will my son need to wear a _____ ?

5. Is _____ the same as football?

6. Many children in the neighborhood _____ sports.

7. There is a large soccer _____ near my house.

8. You need to _____ your daughter after school.

Match Words and Pictures

football	swimming	tennis

1. _____ 2. _____ 3. _____

Underline the Telephone Number You Hear

1. 273-1531	275-1137	273-1351
2. 640-0951	649-0156	640-1590
3. 569-8326	579-8326	569-2683
4. 354-8619	354-8691	355-8619
5. 679-9924	697-9924	699-9924
6. 459-5658	559-5658	459-5856
7. 722-1415	720-1415	726-1415
8. 297-5155	257-4155	275-5154

Write the Prices You Hear

1. _____	8. _____
2. _____	9. _____
3. _____	10. _____
4. _____	11. _____
5. _____	12. _____
6. _____	13. _____
7. _____	14. _____

Underline the Words

Underline each word that has the same vowel sound you hear in the word *time*.

sign	information	uniform	girl
sometimes	child	excited	includes
practice	idea	right	until
quit	his	swimming	birth
Mexico	Kim	tonight	driver
pick	I	certificate	sidewalk

Change the Singular to Plural

Check *s*, *z*, or *iz* to show the correct pronunciation of the final sound.

		s	z	iz
1. youth center	_____	___	___	___
2. cost	_____	___	___	___
3. exercise	_____	___	___	___
4. soccer practice	_____	___	___	___
5. Wednesday	_____	___	___	___
6. football	_____	___	___	___
7. team sport	_____	___	___	___

Write Short Answers

1. Does your son come home at 4:00?   Yes, _____.

2. Is your face dirty?   No, _____.

3. Are you upset?   Yes, _____.

4. Does he want to go to school?   No, _____.

5. Is she surprised?   Yes, _____.

6. Is that boy a nice person?   No, _____.

7. Does he hurt people at school?   Yes, _____.

8. Is your mother angry?   No, _____.

9. Is fighting against school rules?   Yes, _____.

10. Are Fred's parents happy?   No, _____.

Write the One- or Two-Word Comparative

1. My child feels (afraid) _____ at school this year than last year.

2. Fred is (mean) _____ than the other children.

3. Fighting is a (serious) _____ problem at my son's new school than at his old one.

4. I am (upset) _____ by this than before.

Match Words and Pictures

fight	hug	cry

1. _____ 2. _____ 3. _____

Matching: Meanings

____ **1.** dirty   **a.** scared

____ **2.** torn   **b.** hold close

____ **3.** mother   **c.** talk by telephone

____ **4.** afraid   **d.** in violation of

____ **5.** kick   **e.** head of a school

____ **6.** against   **f.** not clean

____ **7.** hug   **g.** strike with the foot

____ **8.** principal   **h.** female parent

____ **9.** shoes   **i.** footwear

____ **10.** call   **j.** ripped

Check the Correct Picture

1.

a. _____ b. _____

3.

a. _____ b. _____

2.

a. _____ b. _____

4.

a. _____ b. _____

Underline the Word You Hear

1. dirty   duty

2. shirts   shorts

3. after   afraid

4. that's   what's

5. anymore   anyone

6. surprise   support

7. huge   hug

8. ruler   rules

9. report   repeat

10. upstairs   upset

11. begin   again

12. cereal   serious

Change the Singular to Plural

Check *s*, *z*, or *iz* to show the correct pronunciation of the final sound.

		s	z	iz
1. dirty face	_____	___	___	___
2. torn shirt	_____	___	___	___
3. kick	_____	___	___	___
4. mother	_____	___	___	___
5. principal	_____	___	___	___
6. young girl	_____	___	___	___
7. broken rule	_____	___	___	___
8. surprise	_____	___	___	___

Underline the Stressed Syllable

principal	librarian	instructor
custodian	secretary	assistant
administrator	supervisor	faculty
president	superintendent	counselor
answer	anymore	serious
information	allowed	suspended

Underline the Correct Verb

1. Iris (is/are) relaxing after school today.

2. (Are/Is) you watching TV?

3. They (don't/doesn't) want to do their homework.

4. After dinner, he (return/returns) to his toys.

5. Her mother and father (say/says), "Do your homework!"

6. The girl (don't/doesn't) want to study right now.

7. (Is/Are) she making funny faces in the mirror?

8. Why (is/are) you wasting time?

9. The children (need/needs) to go to bed soon.

10. We (don't/doesn't) have a lot of time in the morning.

You Write the Question

1. _____ Yes, I am relaxing now.

2. _____ No, I didn't do my homework.

3. _____ Yes, I want to eat dinner.

4. _____ No, I am not wasting time.

5. _____ Yes, my homework is finished.

Underline the Correct Word

1. Iris is (watching/walking) TV.

2. She is playing with (toys/tongues).

3. Iris doesn't want to do (helping/homework).

4. She can do it (later/lately).

5. Iris looks in the (mirror/married).

6. Iris makes funny (first/faces).

7. Her mother is (after/angry) now.

8. She says that Iris is (waiting/wasting) time.

9. Iris wants to do (his/her) homework in the morning.

10. Homework comes before you (wash/watch) TV.

Match Words and Pictures

stuffed animal	board game	blocks

1. _____   2. _____   3. _____

Write the Words You Hear

Listen to the correct spelling of each school subject.
Write each word on the line.

1. _____

2. _____

3. _____

4. _____

5. _____

6. _____

7. _____

8. _____

Underline the Assignment You Hear

1. Chapter 7, pages 84–89   Chapter 11, pages 85–89

2. Questions 1–15   Questions 1–50

3. Lesson 6, pages 18–21   Lesson 16, pages 80–91

4. Worksheets 11 and 12   Worksheets 11 and 14

5. Questions 13–30   Questions 23–30

6. Chapter 10, page 40   Chapter 10, page 14

7. Problems 90–100   Problems 19–100

8. Worksheets 73 and 74   Worksheets 74 and 75

Underline the Words

Underline each word that has the same vowel sound you hear in the word *funny*.

under	brush	studying	ruler
lunch	duplicate	useful	money
purse	returns	music	loud
subway	tongue	schedule	suit
comes	puts	Thursday	student
use	busy	usually	sun

Put these Students in Alphabetical Order by their Last Names

_____ Iris King

_____ Austin Freeman

_____ James Witt

_____ Rachel White

_____ Otto Schulze

_____ Shamar Davis

_____ Bethany Behn

_____ Hai Phan

_____ Robert Scott

_____ Marla Saldana

_____ Lauren Kinney

_____ Isao Yukawa

_____ Willem Grieg

_____ Michelle Lambot

_____ Isela Restova

_____ Ranya Shaarawi

Write Tag Questions

1. This is a spelling test, _____ ?

2. Mrs. Cordua is passing out papers, _____ ?

3. Mike is writing his name and the date, _____ ?

4. The children are listening, _____ ?

5. Tim isn't doing anything, _____ ?

6. He is thinking about recess, _____ ?

7. You want to play ball, _____ ?

8. The first word is *listen*, _____ ?

9. They are not ready, _____ ?

Change *He* to *You*

1. He has a spelling test. _____

2. He writes the date. _____

3. He isn't listening. _____

4. He thinks about recess. _____

5. He doesn't hear the word. _____

6. He needs to listen. _____

Complete the Sentences

directions	passing out	recess	test
number	ready	spelling	words

1. I am not _____! Please repeat number one.

2. We can play ball at _____.

3. Please listen and follow _____.

4. Is the teacher _____ papers?

5. You need to _____ your papers from one to ten.

6. How many _____ will be on the spelling test?

7. Write your name and the date on your _____.

8. We have a _____ test tomorrow. Please study.

Matching: Meanings

____ 1. play   a. instructions

____ 2. directions   b. round object used in games

____ 3. follow   c. try to hear

____ 4. recess   d. have fun

____ 5. ball   e. break from class

____ 6. listen   f. act according to

...rect Picture

b. _____

3.

a. _____   b. _____

2.

a. _____   b. _____

4.

a. _____   b. _____

Write the Words You Hear

1. _____   5. _____

2. _____   6. _____

3. _____   7. _____

4. _____   8. _____

Underline the Words

Underline the words that have the same soft *th* sound you hear in the word *think*.

three	third	then	thirsty
thousand	through	thing	that
thumb	father	thrilled	thank
clothes	throw	youth	math
Thursday	thin	their	teeth
the	those	this	they

Write the Words

Write the words for the numbers 1 through 10.

1. _____   6. _____

2. _____   7. _____

3. _____   8. _____

4. _____   9. _____

5. _____   10. _____

rect Question Word(s)

Where		How long
How		How old

_____ is Mary? | Mary is 6 years old.

_____ does she sleep? | She sleeps 10 hours.

_____ day is tomorrow? | It's Friday.

4. _____ does Mary feel? | She feels sad.

5. _____ stays up late? | Her sister stays up late.

6. _____ does Mary go today? | She goes to school.

Write Each Sentence in the Negative

1. The boy is 12 years old.

_____

2. I need 10 hours of sleep a night.

_____

3. They want to go to bed.

_____

4. She can stay up later tomorrow night.

_____

Underline the Correct Word

1. Adela's (bedroom/bedtime) is 9:00.

2. My daughter needs 10 (horse/hours) of sleep.

3. I need to get up (early/earring) for work.

4. It's time to brush your (teenager/teeth).

5. You have another 10 (minimum/minutes) before bed.

6. I'm not (sleepless/sleepy). Can I stay up?

7. Her son goes to bed later on (Friday/friendly).

8. Your bedtime is 8:00. That's the (rude/rule).

Match Words and Pictures

pajamas	clock	toothbrush

1. _____ **2.** _____ **3.** _____

Verb You Hear

5. feel	feels		
6. have	has		
, on	**7.** go	goes	
stays	**8.** want	wants	

Underline the Time You Hear

1. My children go to bed at (8:15/8:30).

2. It's (7:30/7:45). It's time to brush your teeth.

3. Her sister stays up until about (10:00/10:15).

4. It's (4:20/4:30). What time does the movie start?

5. The bus stops here at (3:30/3:45).

6. Your bedtime is (8:00/9:00).

7. We are eating dinner at (6:00/6:30) tonight.

8. It's (9:30/9:50). Turn off the TV.

Underline the Words

Underline the words that have the same vowel sound you hear in the word *school*.

rule	mother	new	blue
hour	two	full	tooth
soup	brush	put	you
house	good	spoon	door
noon	fruit	food	grow

Rewrite Each Sentence Correctly

1. Marys Bedtime is 8,00.

   _____Mary's bedtime is 8:00._____

2. "you need to be in bed now, says her mother

   _____

3. mary asks, "can I please stay up a little later.

   _____

4. no says marys Mother. your bedtime is right now.

   _____

Write Short Answers

1. Are they at the shopping center?   Yes, _____.

2. Does your son need a new shirt?   No, _____.

3. Does Tamika look at the price tags?   Yes, _____.

4. Is Jamal looking at the cheaper shoes?   No, _____.

5. Are these shoes on sale?   Yes, _____.

6. Is her son looking at the price?   No, _____.

7. Is $100 too much to spend on shoes?   Yes, _____.

8. Are your child's feet still growing?   Yes, _____.

Write Each Sentence in the Negative

1. I need new shoes.

_____

2. There are a lot of shoes here.

_____

3. These shoes are very expensive.

_____

4. He wants the black shoes.

_____

Complete the Sentences

again	expensive	price tag	shoe store
everyone	grow	shakes	spend

1. The _____ is inside the shoe.

2. Mrs. Bradley can't _____ more than $30.

3. Is there a _____ in this shopping center?

4. You are young, so your feet will still _____.

5. Mother _____ her head. She can't pay $100.

6. Jamal wants the shoes that _____ wears.

7. These shoes are too _____. We can't afford them.

8. My feet have grown so I need new shoes _____.

Matching: Opposites

____ 1. work   **a.** below

____ 2. inside   **b.** nobody

____ 3. above   **c.** play

____ 4. everyone   **d.** outside

____ 5. expensive   **e.** false

____ 6. true   **f.** cheap

Check the Correct Picture

1.

a. _____   b. _____

3.

a. _____   b. _____

2.

a. _____   b. _____

4.

a. _____   b. _____

Underline the Price You Hear

1. $33.98 $39.83 $33.89

2. $57.24 $57.42 $52.24

3. $91.40 $19.40 $91.04

4. $12.56 $12.58 $21.58

5. $60.23 $60.32 $60.13

6. $25.72 $52.72 $27.52

7. $83.99 $89.33 $83.33

Complete Each Word with *sh* or *ch*.

Then practice saying the words.

<u>s</u> <u>h</u> oe   __ __ eaper   __ __ ampoo   __ __ apter

__ __ air   __ __ eck   __ __ ort   __ __ annel

__ __ irt   __ __ ange   __ __ art   __ __ arp

__ __ ape   __ __ e   __ __ ild   __ __ ut

__ __ ower   __ __ akes   __ __ eese   __ __ alk

Write the Words

Write the words for the numbers below.

11. _____   20. _____

12. _____   30. _____

13. _____   40. _____

14. _____   50. _____

15. _____   60. _____

16. _____   70. _____

17. _____   80. _____

18. _____   90. _____

19. _____   100. _____

Underline the Correct Verb

1. Natalie and Marie (live/lives) near the school.

2. Do you (need/needs) to cross many streets?

3. My daughter (wait/waits) at every corner.

4. This corner (have/has) a traffic light.

5. Does Ann (see/sees) the "Walk" sign?

6. The children's school (is/are) on a busy street.

7. (Is/Are) there a crosswalk in front of the school?

8. A crossing guard (stand/stands) on the corner.

9. Mr. Ramirez (tell/tells) the children when to cross.

10. No one (want/wants) to get hurt.

You Write the Question

1. _____? No, I don't walk to school.

2. _____? Yes, I wait at the corner.

3. _____? Yes, there is a crosswalk.

4. _____? Yes, I heard a whistle blow.

5. _____? Yes, she is a crossing guard.

Underline the Correct Word

1. Natalie (walks/wakes) to school.

2. She needs to cross many (streets/sheets).

3. She looks to the (leave/left) and to the right.

4. Some corners have (terrific/traffic) lights.

5. Her school is on a (busy/buy) street.

6. A crossing (guard/grand) stands on the corner.

7. He tells children when it is (save/safe) to cross.

8. Natalie doesn't want to get (hurt/heart).

Match Words and Pictures

traffic light	crosswalk	crossing guard

1. _____   2. _____   3. _____

Underline the Verb You Hear

1. push   pushes

2. wait   waits

3. look   looks

4. have   has

5. stand   stands

6. blow   blows

7. tell   tells

8. want   wants

9. walk   walks

10. stop   stops

What Do You Do?

Listen to the tape, and underline what you do.

1. Walk   Don't Walk

2. Walk   Don't Walk

3. Walk   Don't Walk

4. Walk   Don't Walk

5. Walk   Don't Walk

6. Walk   Don't Walk

7. Walk   Don't Walk

8. Walk   Don't Walk

9. Walk   Don't Walk

10. Walk   Don't Walk

Underline the Words

Underline the words that have the same hard *g* sound you hear in the word *guard*.

general	orange	age	gasoline
girls	glasses	gym	gentleman
giraffe	genius	germ	group
gallon	grandfather	grade	ground
eggs	begin	page	growing

Rewrite Each Sentence Correctly

1. remember to wait at every corner

_____

2. i dont cross until I look both ways,

_____

3. please Walk between the two yellow lines?

_____

4. is it safe to cross the street here.

_____

Write Tag Questions

1. Willie doesn't feel well this morning, _____?

2. Katie has a stomachache, _____?

3. You can't go to school today, _____?

4. His father is calling the office, _____?

5. Your last name is Shea, _____?

6. She isn't a third grader, _____?

7. You need to take care of your son, _____?

8. She is giving him some medicine, _____?

9. Willie still has a fever, _____?

10. His mother can stay home tomorrow, _____?

Change *I* to *She*

1. I don't feel well.   _____

2. I have a fever.   _____

3. I need to rest at home.   _____

4. I can't go to school.   _____

5. I call in sick to work.   _____

6. I take some medicine.   _____

Match Words and Pictures

rest at home	call the office	take medicine

1. _____
2. _____
3. _____

Matching: Opposites

____ **1.** absent   **a.** well

____ **2.** first   **b.** a lot

____ **3.** sick   **c.** take

____ **4.** rest   **d.** night

____ **5.** a little   **e.** worse

____ **6.** question   **f.** activity

____ **7.** give   **g.** answer

____ **8.** better   **h.** teacher

____ **9.** day   **i.** present

____ **10.** student   **j.** last

Check the Correct Picture

1.

    a. _____   **b.** _____

3.

    a. _____   **b.** _____

2.

    a. _____   **b.** _____

4.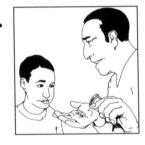

    a. _____   **b.** _____

Write the Number

Listen to the recording, and write the number for each option.

____ Nurse

____ Main office

____ Attendance

____ Directions

____ Principal

____ Teacher

____ Bus garage

____ Library

Complete Each Word with the Vowels
a, e, i, o, or *u*
Then practice saying the words.

v_i_r_u_s   h___d__ch__   c_____gh

s__r__ thr____t   __nf__ct____n   c__ld

f__v__r   r__sh   _____r__ch__

fl__   st__m__ch__ch__   t_____th__ch__

Rewrite Each Sentence Correctly

1. willies father calls the office at school

_____

2. "what is your First Name, asks the clerk

_____

3. Willie rests at home all day?

_____

4. he feels a little better but he still has a fever

_____

5. tomorrow willies mother needs to stay home from work

_____

Listening Exercise Prompts

Lesson 1

Check the Correct Picture (page 6)

1. His mother tells him to get up every morning.
2. Remember to comb your hair.
3. Pick up your backpack before you go.
4. The bus stop is on the corner.

Underline the Time You Hear (page 6)

1. 7:50	**4.** 1:10	**7.** 10:15	**10.** 4:00
2. 3:20	**5.** 3:31	**8.** 12:30	**11.** 11:55
3. 9:40	**6.** 6:45	**9.** 8:27	**12.** 5:00

Lesson 2

Check the Correct Picture (page 10)

1. It is her turn now.
2. Cover your left eye and read the second line.
3. He is pointing to the chart.
4. I'm sending a letter to your parents.

Underline the Word You Hear (page 10)

1. week	**4.** easy	**7.** stop	**10.** nurse
2. sitting	**5.** small	**8.** sees	**11.** ride
3. leave	**6.** fifth	**9.** tired	**12.** eyes

Lesson 3

Check the Correct Picture (page 14)

1. There is a new boy in the class.
2. She turns to her friend.
3. There is still one empty chair.
4. Vanessa feels better now.

Underline the Word You Hear (page 14)

1. It is Juan's first day at school.
2. Is she from Mexico?
3. My daughter is only 11 months old.
4. Everyone in the class speaks English.
5. We have a new teacher.
6. Sit down at table number three.
7. What does that word mean in Spanish?

Lesson 4

Check the Correct Picture (page 18)

1. He is getting ready for school.
2. The bell rings at 7:40.
3. Today they are serving cereal.
4. Remember to throw away your container.

Underline the Word You Hear (page 18)

1. I catch the train at 7:00.
2. Is your mother in the kitchen?
3. Do you have time for some cereal?
4. There is a breakfast program at school.
5. He wants his child to stay healthy.
6. We arrive at school at 7:25.
7. The school cafeteria is on the right.

Lesson 5

Underline the Day and Time You Hear (page 22)

1. His conference is Monday at 11:30.
2. Can you volunteer on Tuesday at 10:30?
3. She is expecting your parents on Wednesday at 2:45.
4. The book fair is on Saturday at 12:00.
5. Your father can come on Friday at 4:45.
6. Back to School Night is Thursday at 6:00.
7. The teacher's earliest conference is Monday at 8:10.
8. I'll see you on Tuesday at 3:30.

Underline the Word You Hear (page 22)

1. Is he in the second grade?
2. I need to talk to your mother.
3. The teacher is concerned about her writing.
4. He needs help with his spelling.
5. Their daughter is behind the other students.
6. She is worried about that too.
7. Reading is very important.
8. Look for a good book about basketball.

Lesson 6

Check the Correct Picture (page 26)

1. Mrs. Ho volunteers in her son's class.
2. That boy is raising his hand.
3. She works with small groups of children.
4. I am proud to see my mother at school.

Complete the Addition Problems You Hear (page 26)

1. 5 + 3	**3.** 8 + 0	**5.** 3 + 4	**7.** 1 + 5
2. 8 + 2	**4.** 6 + 1	**6.** 7 + 3	**8.** 2 + 6

9. 7 + 2 **11.** 0 + 6 **13.** 5 + 4
10. 4 + 4 **12.** 1 + 9 **14.** 6 + 3

Lesson 7

Check the Correct Picture (page 30)

1. Here is your breakfast.
2. The math test begins at 9:30.
3. Please go to bed early.
4. He looks very tired this morning.

Write the Times You Hear (page 30)

1. The test begins at 9:00.
2. We usually have breakfast at 7:30.
3. Please arrive at school by 8:15.
4. You need to be in bed at 8:30.
5. There will be a science test tomorrow at 10:00.
6. It's 11:00. The test is over.
7. Can you pick him up at 3:00 today?
8. Juan was here at 8:00 yesterday morning.
9. It's 6:30. What do you want for breakfast?
10. We need to leave at exactly 7:00.
11. Does the last test begin at 10:30?
12. It's 12:00. We can stop for today.
13. The math test begins at 1:45.
14. Your father will pick you up at 4:30.

Lesson 8

Underline the Telephone Number You Hear (page 34)

1. 273-1351   **5.** 679-9924
2. 640-0951   **6.** 559-5658
3. 579-8326   **7.** 726-1415
4. 354-8691   **8.** 297-5155

Write the Prices You Hear (page 34)

1. The basketball league charges $45.
2. The soccer shoes are $22.
3. The uniform costs $25.
4. Are the balls $19 each?
5. The gym costs are $30 a month.
6. You can buy a helmet like this for $27.
7. These long socks are $4 a pair.
8. The team swimsuit is $38.
9. Gymnastics costs $40 a month.
10. Each aerobics class is $6.
11. It costs $3 to swim at the public pool.
12. Youth baseball is $85 for the season.
13. I need $11 for a team shirt.
14. The total comes to $51.

Lesson 9

Check the Correct Picture (page 38)

1. His face isn't dirty.   **3.** Why are you crying?
2. Her shirt is torn.   **4.** His mother gives him a hug.

Underline the Word You Hear (page 38)

1. dirty   **4.** what's   **7.** huge   **10.** upstairs
2. shorts   **5.** anyone   **8.** rules   **11.** again
3. after   **6.** surprise   **9.** repeat   **12.** cereal

Lesson 10

Write the Words You Hear (page 42)

1. math: m-a-t-h
2. science: s-c-i-e-n-c-e
3. language: l-a-n-g-u-a-g-e
4. handwriting: h-a-n-d-w-r-i-t-i-n-g
5. social studies: s-o-c-i-a-l s-t-u-d-i-e-s
6. geography: g-e-o-g-r-a-p-h-y
7. spelling: s-p-e-l-l-i-n-g
8. reading: r-e-a-d-i-n-g

Underline the Assignment You Hear (page 42)

1. Chapter 11, pages 85-89
2. Questions 1 through 50
3. Lesson 6, pages 18 through 21
4. Worksheets 11 and 12
5. Questions 23 through 30
6. Chapter 10, page 40
7. Problems 90 through 100
8. Worksheets 74 and 75

Lesson 11

Check the Correct Picture (page 46)

1. The teacher is passing out papers.
2. Larry is writing the date.
3. Number your papers from 1 to 15.
4. It's time for the test.

Write the Words You Hear (page 46)

1. listen   **3.** spell   **5.** follow   **7.** children
2. paper   **4.** pencil   **6.** sorry   **8.** recess

Lesson 12

Underline the Verb You Hear (page 50)

1. need   **3.** put on   **5.** feels   **7.** goes
2. tell   **4.** stays   **6.** have   **8.** wants

Underline the Time You Hear (page 50)

1. My children go to bed at 8:30.
2. It's 7:45. It's time to brush your teeth.
3. Her sister stays up until about 10:00.
4. It's 4:30. What time does the movie start?
5. The bus stops here at 3:45.
6. Your bedtime is 8:00.
7. We are eating dinner at 6:00 tonight.
8. It's 9:30. Turn off the TV.

Lesson 13

Check the Correct Picture (page 54)

1. My son needs new shoes.
2. He jumps up and down and says, "Please!"
3. Her shoes are too small.
4. Their daughter is angry.

Underline the Price You Hear (page 54)

1. $33.89	3. $19.40	5. $60.32	7. $83.99
2. $57.42	4. $12.56	6. $27.52	

Lesson 14

Underline the Verb You Hear (page 58)

1. pushes	3. look	5. stands	7. tells	9. walks
2. waits	4. has	6. blows	8. want	10. stop

What Do You Do? (page 58)

1. A car is coming.
2. It's OK to go.
3. Watch out for the truck.

4. The crossing guard stopped the traffic.
5. It's clear now.
6. You can cross safely.
7. Wait! The light is red.
8. Be careful. That bus is turning.
9. The sign says, "Don't walk."
10. The crossing guard says it's safe to cross.

Lesson 15

Check the Correct Picture (page 62)

1. Her daughter has a fever.
2. She needs to rest today.
3. Her father needs to stay home from work.
4. Here is some medicine for your fever.

Write the Number (page 62)

You have reached River Park Elementary School. Listen carefully to the following options. To leave a message for a teacher, press 1. To speak to someone in the attendance office, press 2. To leave a message for the principal, press 3. For the school nurse, press 4. For the library, press 5. To reach the bus garage, press 6. To get directions to the school, press 7. To speak to the operator in the main office, press 0. Thank you.

Answer Key

Lesson 1

Underline the Correct Verb (page 4)

1. feel	5. looks	9. stops, opens
2. don't	6. brushes	10. Are
3. want	7. run	
4. don't want	8. yell	

You Write the Question (page 4)

1. Do you feel tired today?
2. Do you want to get up?
3. Does the bus come at 7:15?
4. Is the bus leaving?
5. Are you lucky this time?

Match Words and Pictures (page 5)

1. comb hair   2. get dressed   3. brush teeth

Matching: Opposites (page 5)

1. f	5. a	9. j
2. g	6. h	10. e
3. i	7. d	
4. c	8. b	

Check the Correct Picture (page 6)

1. b	2. b	3. a	4. b

Underline the Time You Hear (page 6)

1. 7:50	4. 1:10	7. 10:15	10. 4:00
2. 3:20	5. 3:31	8. 12:30	11. 11:55
3. 9:40	6. 6:45	9. 8:27	12. 5:00

How Is the *e* Pronounced? (page 7)

feels
1. be
2. begins
3. eats
4. need
5. sees
6. sleep
7. teeth

get
1. bed
2. breakfast
3. dressed
4. Emily
5. opens
6. yellow
7. yells

Matching: Times (page 7)

1. d   2. f   3. a   4. b   5. e   6. c

Lesson 2

Write Short Answers (page 8)

1. Yes, she is.
2. No, it's not. OR No, it isn't.
3. Yes, I am.
4. No, it's not. OR No, it isn't.
5. Yes, they are.
6. No, I can't.
7. Yes, I do.
8. No, they don't.
9. Yes, it is.
10. No, she doesn't.

Write the One-Word Comparative (page 8)

1. easier   2. bigger   3. clearer   4. smaller

Underline the Correct Word (page 9)

1. exam
2. turn
3. right
4. second
5. chart
6. board
7. wrong
8. headache
9. parents
10. eye

Matching: Meanings (page 9)

1. b   2. d   3. f   4. g   5. e   6. c   7. a

Check the Correct Picture (page 10)

1. b   2. a   3. a   4. b

Underline the Word You Hear (page 10)

1. week
2. sitting
3. leave
4. easy
5. small
6. fifth
7. stop
8. sees
9. tired
10. nurse
11. ride
12. eyes

How is the Final *s* Pronounced? (page 11)

s
1. charts
2. headaches
3. points
4. stops
5. weeks

z
1. covers
2. exams
3. lines
4. reads
5. sometimes

Write the Words (page 11)

1. first
2. second
3. third
4. fourth
5. fifth
6. sixth
7. seventh
8. eighth
9. ninth
10. tenth

Lesson 3

Write the Correct Question Word (page 12)

1. Where   3. How   5. Where
2. How   4. Who   6. Who

Change *She* to *They* (page 12)

1. They are 8 years old.
2. They are from Russia.
3. They see many children.
4. They feel shy.
5. They sit at table three.
6. They have a new friend.

Match Words and Pictures (page 13)

1. point to chair   2. enter class   3. sit down

Matching: Opposites (page 13)

1. i   3. a   5. e   7. c   9. b
2. d   4. h   6. j   8. f   10. g

Check the Correct Picture (page 14)

1. b   2. a   3. a   4. a

Underline the Word You Hear (page 14)

1. first   3. months   5. teacher   7. Spanish
2. she   4. Everyone   6. three

How Is the *a* Pronounced? (page 15)

late
1. came
2. day
3. name
4. states
5. table
6. today

at
1. can
2. class
3. have
4. last
5. Spanish
6. understand

Underline the Stressed Syllable (page 15)

<u>Mex</u>ico   <u>emp</u>ty   <u>a</u>cross   <u>speak</u>ing
Ja<u>pan</u>   be<u>gin</u>   <u>Eng</u>lish   u<u>nit</u>ed
<u>eve</u>ryone   Japa<u>nese</u>   under<u>stand</u>   <u>wel</u>come
<u>teach</u>er   <u>lan</u>guage   <u>wor</u>ry

Lesson 4

Write Tag Questions (page 16)

1. aren't you?
2. don't we?
3. doesn't he?
4. do I?
5. isn't he?
6. don't you?
7. doesn't she?
8. is he?
9. don't they?

Change *He* to *We* (page 16)

1. We are getting ready now.
2. We need to leave early.
3. We have no time to eat.
4. We are going to eat later.

5. We ride the school bus.

6. We are very hungry today.

Match Words and Pictures (page 17)

1. catch the bus

2. throw it away

3. leave the house

Matching: Meanings (page 17)

1. d	**3.** g	**5.** a	**7.** f	**9.** c
2. h	**4.** e	**6.** j	**8.** b	**10.** i

Check the Correct Picture (page 18)

1. a	**2.** a	**3.** a	**4.** a

Underline the Word You Hear (page 18)

1. train	**3.** cereal	**5.** child	**7.** school
2. mother	**4.** program	**6.** arrive	

Underline the Stressed Syllable (page 19)

<u>hun</u>gry	a<u>way</u>	<u>cer</u>eal	con<u>tain</u>er
<u>break</u>fast	attention	<u>Tues</u>day	<u>daugh</u>ter
<u>of</u>fice	<u>heal</u>thy	to<u>day</u>	<u>men</u>u
<u>some</u>thing	be<u>gin</u>	ba<u>na</u>na	

Change the Singular to Plural (page 19)

1. yellow houses	iz
2. new schools	z
3. buses	iz
4. empty bowls	z
5. heavy backpacks	s
6. programs	z
7. healthy sons	z
8. good students	s
9. full glasses	iz

Lesson 5

Underline the Correct Verb (page 20)

1. is	**4.** am	**7.** need	**10.** takes
2. Are	**5.** feels	**8.** don't	
3. helps	**6.** Are	**9.** are	

You Write the Question (page 20)

1. Is the conference today?

2. Is she his teacher?

3. Are you proud of your child?

4. Does he read at home?

5. Can you check out books?

Complete the Sentences (page 21)

1. third	**3.** readers	**5.** help
2. classroom	**4.** library	**6.** return

Match Words and Pictures (page 21)

1. Math	**2.** Handwriting	**3.** Reading

Underline the Day and Time You Hear (page 22)

1. Monday at 11:30	**5.** Friday at 4:45
2. Tuesday at 10:30	**6.** Thursday at 6:00
3. Wednesday at 2:45	**7.** Monday at 8:10
4. Saturday at 12:00	**8.** Tuesday at 3:30

Underline the Word You Hear (page 22)

1. second	**3.** writing	**5.** behind	**7.** important
2. mother	**4.** spelling	**6.** worried	**8.** basketball

Underline the Words (page 23)

sitting	important	miss	interesting
difficult	principal	inches	little

Put these Authors in Alphabetical Order (page 23)

5	11	6	21	15	7	8
3	9	14	17	13	4	2
1	19	12	18	20	10	16

Lesson 6

Write Short Answers (page 24)

1. Yes, she does.

2. No, he's not. OR No, he isn't

3. No, she isn't. OR No, she's not.

4. Yes, she does.

5. No, I don't.

6. No, I can't.

Write Each Sentence in the Negative (page 24)

1. His daughter isn't in the fifth grade.

2. She doesn't volunteer in her son's class.

3. He can't come on Tuesday.

4. They don't understand the problem.

5. I can't correct these papers.

Complete the Sentences (page 25)

1. raise	**3.** grade	**5.** volunteer	**7.** corrects
2. time	**4.** proud	**6.** flashcard	**8.** groups

Matching: Days (page 25)

1. d	**3.** a	**5.** b	**7.** c
2. g	**4.** f	**6.** e	

Check the Correct Picture (page 26)

1. b	**2.** a	**3.** b	**4.** a

Fill in the Addition Problems You Hear (page 26)

1. 5+3	**5.** 3+4	**9.** 7+2	**13.** 5+4
2. 8+2	**6.** 7+3	**10.** 4+4	**14.** 6+3
3. 8+0	**7.** 1+5	**11.** 0+6	
4. 6+1	**8.** 2+6	**12.** 1+9	

Underline the Words (page 27)

| wake | raises | papers | maybe |
| radio | phrase | aide | explain |

Change the Singular to Plural (page 27)

1. small groups   s
2. classrooms   z
3. active volunteers   z
4. difficult problems   z
5. flashcards   z
6. grades   z
7. questions   z
8. addition facts   s
9. proud parents   s

Lesson 7

Write the Correct Question Word(s) (page 28)

1. What   3. When   5. How long   7. Who
2. Who   4. What   6. Where   8. When

Write the Two-Word Comparative (page 28)

1. more difficult   3. more nutritious
2. more important   4. more tired

Match Words and Pictures (page 29)

1. breakfast   2. backpack   3. bedroom

Matching: Meanings (page 29)

1. b   4. h   7. d   10. i
2. e   5. c   8. f
3. a   6. g   9. j

Check the Correct Picture (page 30)

1. b   2. a   3. a   4. a

Write the Times You Hear (page 30)

1. 9:00   5. 10:00   9. 6:30   13. 1:45
2. 7:30   6. 11:00   10. 7:00   14. 4:30
3. 8:15   7. 3:00   11. 10:30
4. 8:30   8. 8:00   12. 12:00

Underline the Words (page 31)

opens	note	low	road
phone	only	home	
those	also	notebook	

Underline the Stressed Syllable (page 31)

backpack	suggests	student	result
activity	ready	Friday	understand
material	permission	language	difficult
principal	announcement	arrive	
information	volunteer	important	

Lesson 8

Write Tag Questions (page 32)

1. doesn't he?   6. don't they?
2. can't she?   7. do you?
3. isn't it?   8. does he?
4. aren't they?   9. doesn't he?
5. doesn't she?   10. can't you?

Change *He* to *I* (page 32)

1. I pick up Marla.   4. I don't know the cost.
2. I see children playing.   5. I need more information.
3. I buy a soccer ball.   6. I can't say yes or no.

Complete the Sentences (page 33)

1. cost   3. time   5. soccer   7. field
2. parents   4. uniform   6. play   8. pick up

Match Words and Pictures (page 33)

1. tennis   2. swimming   3. football

Underline the Telephone Number You Hear (page 34)

1. 273-1351   5. 679-9924
2. 640-0951   6. 559-5658
3. 579-8326   7. 726-1415
4. 354-8691   8. 297-5155

Write the Prices You Hear (page 34)

1. $45   5. $30   9. $40   13. $11
2. $22   6. $27   10. $6   14. $51
3. $25   7. $4   11. $3
4. $19   8. $38   12. $85

Underline the Words (page 35)

sign	idea	excited	driver
sometimes	I	right	sidewalk
child		tonight	

Change the Singular to Plural (page 35)

1. youth centers   z
2. costs   s
3. exercises   iz
4. soccer practices   iz
5. Wednesdays   z
6. footballs   z
7. team sports   s

Lesson 9

Write Short Answers (page 36)

1. Yes, he does.
2. No, it isn't. OR No, it's not.
3. Yes, I am.

4. No, he doesn't.

5. Yes, she is.

6. No, he's not. OR No, he isn't.

7. Yes, he does.

8. No, she's not. OR No, she isn't.

9. Yes, it is.

10. No, they're not. OR No, they aren't.

Write the One- or Two-Word Comparative (page 36)

1. more afraid

2. meaner

3. more serious

4. more upset

Match Words and Pictures (page 37)

1. cry   **2.** fight   **3.** hug

Matching: Meanings (page 37)

1. f   **4.** a   **7.** b   **10.** c

2. j   **5.** g   **8.** e

3. h   **6.** d   **9.** i

Check the Correct Picture (page 38)

1. b   **2.** b   **3.** a   **4.** b

Underline the Word You Hear (page 38)

1. dirty   **4.** what's   **7.** huge   **10.** upstairs

2. shorts   **5.** anyone   **8.** rules   **11.** again

3. after   **6.** surprise   **9.** repeat   **12.** cereal

Change the Singular to Plural (page 39)

1. dirty faces   iz

2. torn shirts   s

3. kicks   s

4. mothers   z

5. principals   z

6. young girls   z

7. broken rules   z

8. surprises   iz

Underline the Stressed Syllable (page 39)

principal   information   anymore   counselor

custodian   librarian   allowed   serious

administrator   secretary   instructor   suspended

president   supervisor   assistant

answer   superintendent   faculty

Lesson 10

Underline the Correct Verb (page 40)

1. is   **4.** returns   **7.** Is   **10.** don't

2. Are   **5.** say   **8.** are

3. don't   **6.** doesn't   **9.** need

You Write the Question (page 40)

1. Are you relaxing now?

2. Did you do your homework?

3. Do you want to eat dinner?

4. Are you wasting time?

5. Is your homework finished?

Underline the Correct Word (page 41)

1. watching   **4.** later   **7.** angry   **10.** watch

2. toys   **5.** mirror   **8.** wasting

3. homework   **6.** faces   **9.** her

Match Words and Pictures (page 41)

1. board game   **2.** stuffed animal   **3.** blocks

Write the Words You Hear (page 42)

1. math   **4.** handwriting   **7.** spelling

2. science   **5.** social studies   **8.** reading

3. language   **6.** geography

Underline the Assignment You Hear (page 42)

1. Chapter 11, pages 85–89

2. Questions 1–50

3. Lesson 6, pages 18–21

4. Worksheets 11 and 12

5. Questions 23–30

6. Chapter 10, page 40

7. Problems 90–100

8. Worksheets 74 and 75

Underline the Words (page 43)

under   comes   studying

lunch   brush   money

subway   tongue   sun

Put these Students in Alphabetical Order by their Last Names (page 43)

5	12
3	10
15	6
14	16
11	4
2	7
1	9
8	13

Lesson 11

Write Tag Questions (page 44)

1. isn't it?   **4.** aren't they?   **7.** don't you?

2. isn't she?   **5.** is he?   **8.** isn't it?

3. isn't he?   **6.** isn't he?   **9.** are they?

Change *He* to *You* (page 44)

1. You have a spelling test.

2. You write the date.

3. You aren't listening.

4. You think about recess.

5. You don't hear the word.

6. You need to listen.

Complete the Sentences (page 45)

1. ready   **3.** directions   **5.** number   **7.** test

2. recess   **4.** passing out   **6.** words   **8.** spelling

Matching: Meanings (page 45)

1. d   **2.** a   **3.** f   **4.** e   **5.** b   **6.** c

Check the Correct Picture (page 46)

1. a   **2.** b   **3.** b   **4.** b

Write the Words You Hear (page 46)

1. listen   **3.** spell   **5.** follow   **7.** children

2. paper   **4.** pencil   **6.** sorry   **8.** recess

Underline the Words (page 47)

three	third	thing	thank
thousand	through	thrilled	math
thumb	throw	youth	teeth
Thursday	thin	thirsty	

Write the Words (page 47)

1. one   **4.** four   **7.** seven   **10.** ten

2. two   **5.** five   **8.** eight

3. three   **6.** six   **9.** nine

Lesson 12

Write the Correct Question Word(s) (page 48)

1. How old   **3.** What   **5.** Who

2. How long   **4.** How   **6.** Where

Write Each Sentence in the Negative (page 48)

1. The boy is not 12 years old.

2. I don't need 10 hours of sleep a night.

3. They don't want to go to bed.

4. She can't stay up later tomorrow night.

Underline the Correct Word (page 49)

1. bedtime   **3.** early   **5.** minutes   **7.** Friday

2. hours   **4.** teeth   **6.** sleepy   **8.** rule

Match Words and Pictures (page 49)

1. clock   **2.** toothbrush   **3.** pajamas

Underline the Verb You Hear (page 50)

1. need   **3.** put on   **5.** feels   **7.** goes

2. tell   **4.** stays   **6.** have   **8.** wants

Underline the Time You Hear (page 50)

1. 8:30   **3.** 10:00   **5.** 3:45   **7.** 6:00

2. 7:45   **4.** 4:30   **6.** 8:00   **8.** 9:30

Underline the Words (page 51)

rule	two	spoon	tooth
soup	fruit	food	you
noon	new	blue	

Rewrite Each Sentence Correctly (page 51)

1. Mary's bedtime is 8:00.

2. "You need to be in bed now," says her mother.

3. Mary asks, "Can I please stay up a little later?"

4. "No," says Mary's mother. "Your bedtime is right now."

Lesson 13

Write Short Answers (page 52)

1. Yes, they are.

2. No, he doesn't.

3. Yes, she does.

4. No, he's not. OR No, he isn't.

5. Yes, they are.

6. No, he's not. OR No, he isn't.

7. Yes, it is.

8. Yes, they are.

Write Each Sentence in the Negative (page 52)

1. I don't need new shoes.

2. There aren't a lot of shoes here.

3. These shoes aren't very expensive.

4. He doesn't want the black shoes.

Complete the Sentences (page 53)

1. price tag **3.** shoe store **5.** shakes **7.** expensive

2. spend   **4.** grow   **6.** everyone **8.** again

Matching: Opposites (page 53)

1. c   **2.** d   **3.** a   **4.** b   **5.** f   **6.** e

Check the Correct Picture (page 54)

1. a   **2.** b   **3.** b   **4.** b

Underline the Price You Hear (page 54)

1. $33.89   **3.** $19.40   **5.** $60.32   **7.** $83.99

2. $57.42   **4.** $12.56   **6.** $27.52

Complete Each Word with *sh* or *ch* (page 55)

shoe	cheaper	shampoo	chapter
chair	check	short	channel
shirt	change	chart	sharp
shape	she	child	shut
shower	shakes	cheese	chalk

Write the Words (page 55)

11. eleven	17. seventeen	50. fifty`
12. twelve	18. eighteen	60. sixty
13. thirteen	19. nineteen	70. seventy
14. fourteen	20. twenty	80. eighty
15. fifteen	30. thirty	90. ninety
16. sixteen	40. forty	100. one hundred

Lesson 14

Underline the Correct Verb (page 56)

1. live	4. has	7. Is	10. wants
2. need	5. see	8. stands	
3. waits	6. is	9. tells	

You Write the Question (page 56)

1. Do you walk to school?
2. Do you wait at the corner?
3. Is there a crosswalk?
4. Did you hear a whistle blow?
5. Is she a crossing guard?

Underline the Correct Word (page 57)

1. walks	3. left	5. busy	7. safe
2. streets	4. traffic	6. guard	8. hurt

Match Words and Pictures (page 57)

1. crossing guard   2. traffic light   3. crosswalk

Underline the Verb You Hear (page 58)

1. pushes	3. look	5. stands	7. tells	9. walks
2. waits	4. has	6. blows	8. want	10. stop

What Do You Do? (page 58)

1. Don't Walk	4. Walk	7. Don't Walk	10. Walk
2. Walk	5. Walk	8. Don't Walk	
3. Don't Walk	6. Walk	9. Don't Walk	

Underline the Words (page 59)

girls	glasses	grade	ground
gallon	grandfather	gasoline	growing
eggs	begin	group	

Rewrite Each Sentence Correctly (page 59)

1. Remember to wait at every corner.
2. I don't cross until I look both ways.
3. Please walk between the two yellow lines.
4. Is it safe to cross the street here?

Lesson 15

Write Tag Questions (page 60)

1. does he?	5. isn't it?	9. doesn't he?
2. doesn't she?	6. is she?	10. can't she?
3. can you?	7. don't you?	
4. isn't he?	8. isn't she?	

Change I to She (page 60)

1. She doesn't feel well.
2. She has a fever.
3. She needs to rest at home.
4. She can't go to school.
5. She calls in sick to work.
6. She takes some medicine.

Match Words and Pictures (page 61)

1. call the office   2. rest at home   3. take medicine

Matching: Opposites (page 61)

1. i	4. f	7. c	10. h
2. j	5. b	8. e	
3. a	6. g	9. d	

Check the Correct Picture (page 62)

1. a	2. a	3. a	4. a

Write the Number (page 62)

4 Nurse	7 Directions	6 Bus garage
0 Main office	3 Principal	5 Library
2 Attendance	1 Teacher	

Complete Each Word with the Vowels *a*, *e*, *i*, *o*, or *u* (page 63)

virus	headache	cough
sore throat	infection	cold
fever	rash	earache
flu	stomachache	toothache

Rewrite Each Sentence Correctly (page 63)

1. Willie's father calls the office at school.
2. "What is your first name?" asks the clerk.
3. Willie rests at home all day.
4. He feels a little better, but he still has a fever.
5. Tomorrow Willie's mother needs to stay home from work.